What Else Can I Pl
Piano
Preparatory Grade

Series Editor: Miranda Steel

Music arranged and processed by
Barnes Music Engraving Ltd
East Sussex TN22 4HA, England

Cover design by Headline Publicity

Published 2000

Introduction

In this *What Else Can I Play?* collection you'll find eighteen popular tunes that are both challenging and entertaining.

The pieces have been carefully selected and arranged to create ideal supplementary material for young pianists who are either working towards or have recently taken a Preparatory Test.

Technical demands increase progressively, gradually introducing new concepts that reflect the requirements of the major examination boards. Each piece offers suggestions and guidelines to fingering, dynamics and tempo, together with technical tips and performance notes.

Pupils will experience a wide variety of music, ranging from classical and jazz through to showtunes and popular songs, leading to a greater awareness of musical styles.

Whether it's for light relief from examination preparation, or to reinforce the understanding of new concepts, this collection will enthuse and encourage all young pianists.

Amazing grace

Traditional

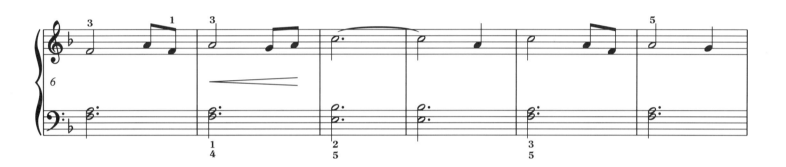

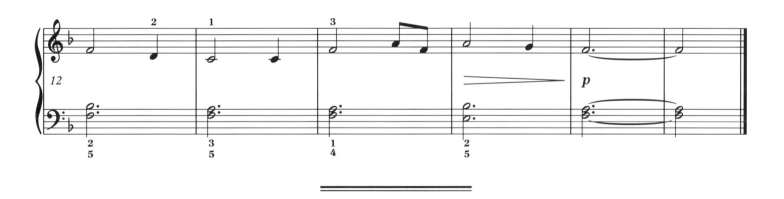

This melody is thought to have its origins in an early American folk tune, but it is much better known as the music to the hymn it is named after. The words of the hymn were written by John Newton, who was a sea captain and slave trader before he became a church minister.

Play this with as smooth and *cantabile* (singing style) a right hand as possible, especially when changing hand position.

4

On the sunny side of the street

Music by Jimmy McHugh

This song comes from the 1930 Broadway musical *International Revue*. Its composer, Jimmy McHugh, wrote an extraordinary number of songs. His compositions included songs for over 50 films in the 1930s and 40s. During World War II he wrote songs encouraging Americans to lend money to their government to help with the war effort.

The tune in this piece is shared between both hands, so make sure you match the dynamics and phrasing between them. Watch out for the changes of hand position in bars 5 and 6 – the hands get quite close here!

Doo dah

Music by Toonie, Sponge and Shooter

This is one of the tracks on the Cartoons' album 'Toonage'. Their music has been nicknamed plastic rock 'n' roll and technobilly, but this song is more like a hoedown. The band members wear enormous wigs and include two Elvis dress-alikes called Puddy and Boop.

The tune in this song is shared between the two hands; they tend to take turns with the tune, as if two different singers were performing it. Good luck with bar 9 – it's not easy and may need some practice.

Theme from Waltz
(from 'The Sleeping Beauty')

Music by Tchaichovsky

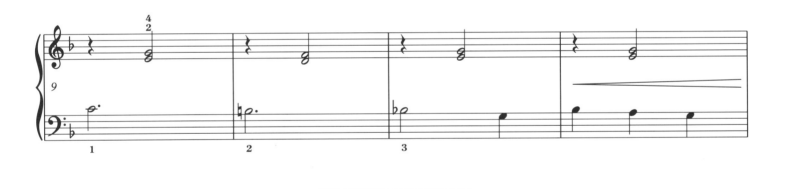

Tchaikovsky was a Russian composer who lived in the nineteenth century. His father was an inspector of mines and he was himself a civil servant before he turned his hand to music full time. Even so he had to supplement his income as a composer by teaching until he was almost forty.

This is a waltz, which is a dance with three beats in the bar that correspond to foot movements. However, if you can, you should think of it as having one beat in a bar – in other words, one bar is one beat. This way you'll give a wonderful flow to the tune, which is in the left hand.

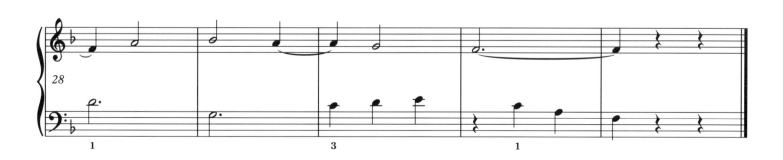

Theme from Pomp and Circumstance

Music by Elgar

Majestically (♩ = 88)

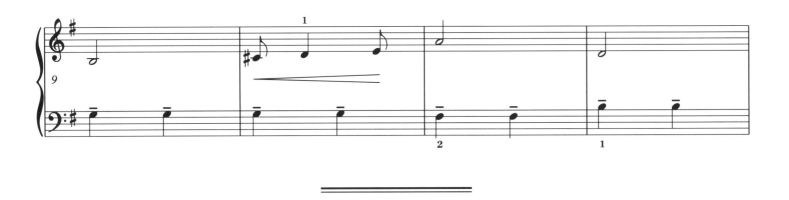

'Pomp and Circumstance' was the name that Elgar gave to five of his marches for orchestra. The name came from the third act of the Shakespeare play *Othello*. Words were written to this one which now makes it thought of as typically English and popular at the Proms. It has become popularly known by the first line of the words: 'Land of Hope and Glory'.

The left hand here needs a long, steady tone – this is a march, after all! There are some odd rhythms in the right hand, which may seem awkward at first, but will soon become second nature. Have fun with the final *crescendo* (gradually getting louder).

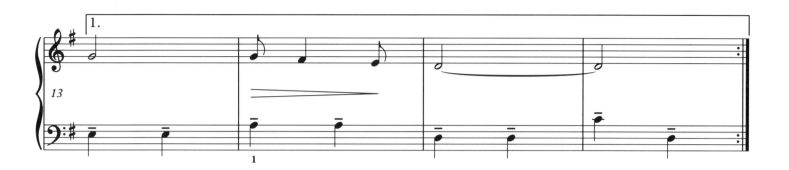

rit.

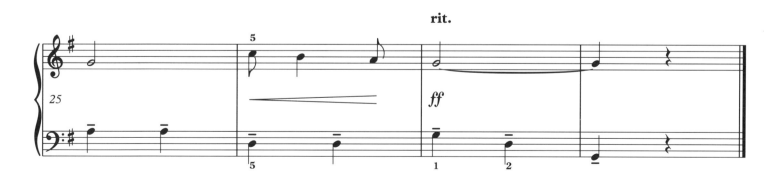

This is my lovely day

Words by Alan Herbert, Music by Vivian Ellis

Moderately ($\quarternote$ = 120)

This song is from a stage musical called *Bless the Bride* set in Victorian England, which opened in London just after World War II. Vivian Ellis also wrote a song called 'Spread a Little Happiness' which was a hit when it was recorded by Sting, over fifty years after it was written.

Make the most of the dynamics (louds and softs) in the piece; really exaggerate the *crescendos* (gradually getting louder) and *diminuendos* (gradually getting softer). There are a few tricky fingerings to watch out for, especially in the left hand.

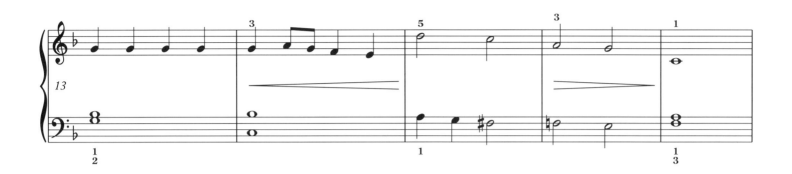

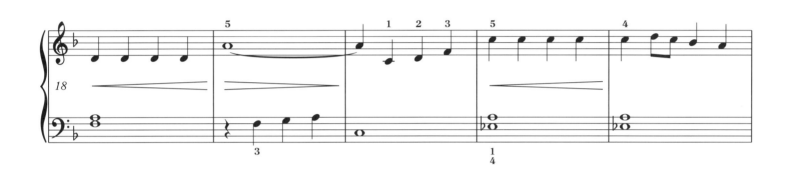

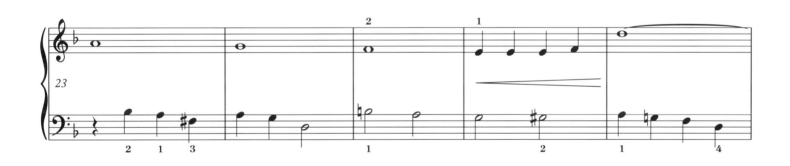

Let there be love

Words by Ian Murray Seafield, Music by Lionel Rand

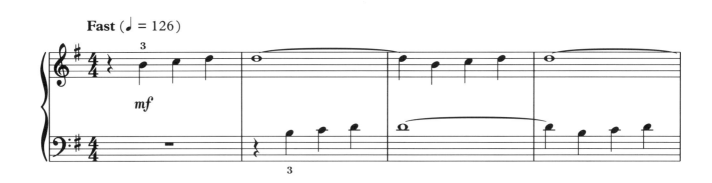

Although several people have recorded this song, it is probably most closely linked with the American singer Nat King Cole. Best known for his mellow expressive voice, Cole started out as a pianist and appeared in several films.

In the song, the right hand and left hand take turns at being important. This is because the tune, starting in the right hand, is then imitated in the left hand, so make sure you match the phrasing. This technique of one hand copying the other is often called 'question and answer'.

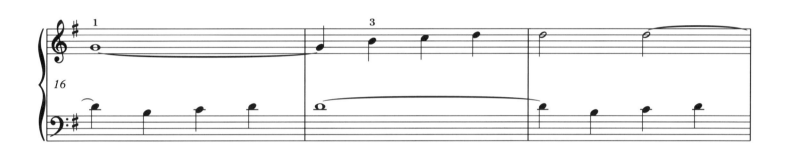

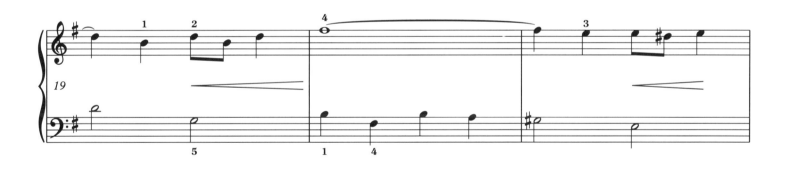

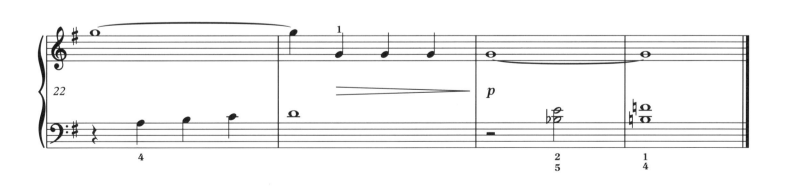

Theme from Can-Can
(from 'La Vie Parisienne')

Music by Offenbach

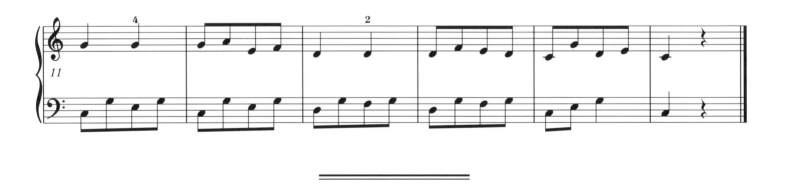

The Can-Can was a fast and acrobatic dance popular in Paris in the nineteenth century where the composer, Offenbach, lived and worked. Offenbach wrote what was then thought to be lightweight work for the stage. Because it was different from traditional music, and shorter than opera, his works are called operettas.

The left hand in this piece is an example of something called *alberti bass* – broken chords in repeating patterns. Once you've mastered the right hand tune (which is fairly easy if you know your scales), you can play this one faster and faster. The faster it is, the better it sounds!

Bob the builder

Words and Music by Paul K Joyce

Bob the Builder is an animated children's programme. Bob is an absent-minded builder whose friends are a gang of talking construction vehicles who live in Bob's yard.

The first and last four bars of this piece have some tricky fingerings in the right hand, so practise it slowly at first – you'll soon get the hang of it. Note the difference in dynamics between the chorus (the first and last four bars) and the verse (the middle eight bars).

Southampton (from 'Titanic')

Words and Music by James Horner

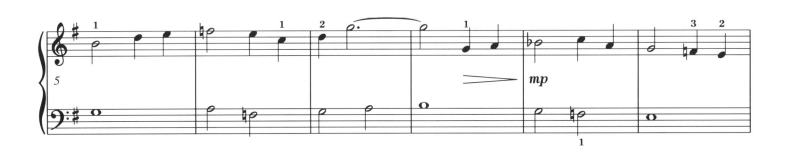

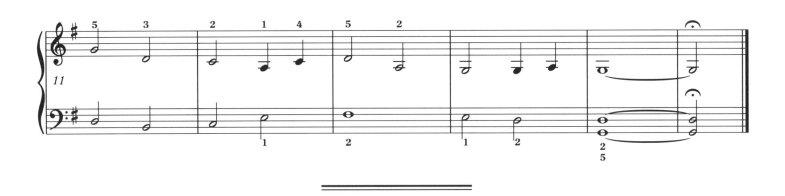

This is from the film *Titanic* starring Leonardo DiCaprio and Kate Winslet. The composer James Horner won an Oscar for his music for the film. It was the first film score to get to No. 1 in the American charts in twenty years.

This piece is an example of *two-part counterpoint*. What this means is that both hands have melodies in them, and although the right hand is more important, the left hand should sound just as melodic and cantabile.

In our lifetime

Words and Music by John McElhone and Sharleen Spiteri

'In Our Lifetime' was co-written by Sharleen Spiteri, lead singer with the band Texas. Despite their name the band come from Glasgow. They are named after one of Sharleen's favourite films, called *Paris, Texas*. 'In Our Lifetime' is on the album 'The Hush'.

The left hand here plays chords (i.e. more than one note at a time), which need to be carefully controlled, so that one note isn't louder than the other.

God save the Queen

Traditional

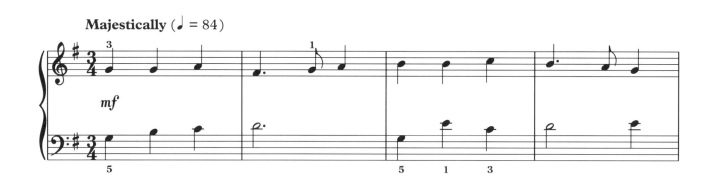

The British national anthem has been named the best-known tune in the world. When America broke away from British rule, the Americans adopted it too, but with different words. In fact many composers have used it in their work, including Brahms and Beethoven.

Although the tune is in the right hand, and needs all the majesty and pomp of a royal occasion, watch the left hand: there are some difficult leaps in bars 3 and 11.

Daisy Bell

Words and Music by Harry Dacre

'Daisy Bell' was written over 100 years ago. The English composer Harry Dacre was living in America when he wrote it, but it wasn't well known until it became a big music-hall hit back in England.

Don't worry about the look of this piece – it's not as strange as it seems! The tune moves between the two hands, so matching the dynamics and making the melody flow are the most important points. Think of your two hands as one ten-fingered hand!

The rose

Words and Music by Amanda McBroom

This is the title song of the 1979 film *The Rose*. It was recorded by the star of the film, Bette Midler and became a number one hit. The composer, Amanda McBroom, is a noted singer and songwriter, with several albums to her credit. She has also appeared on TV in such programs as *Star Trek: The Next Generation*, *Hawaii Five-O* and *M*A*S*H*.

The timing is slightly tricky in this piece, so you will need to count quite carefully. Notice the alternative fingering for the left hand in bar 2 – try both, see which is more comfortable.

Stranger on the shore

Music by Acker Bilk

This piece was a remarkable hit for Acker Bilk in 1962 when it topped the charts in both the UK and the US. In the UK it was in the best-sellers list for 55 weeks! Acker Bilk's real name is Bernard Stanley Bilk, but he was given the nickname 'Acker', which is a Somerset term that means 'friend' or 'mate'.

Note that both hands are written in the treble clef – the hands get quite close together at times. The left hand takes one note of the main melody in bars 4 and 12, but otherwise is playing its own melody as an accompaniment.

As time goes by

Words and Music by Herman Hupfeld

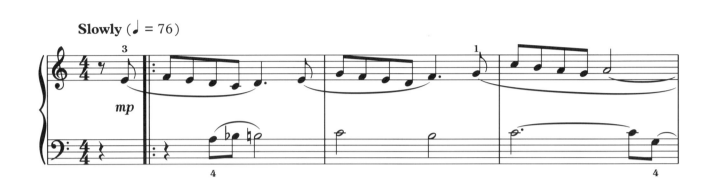

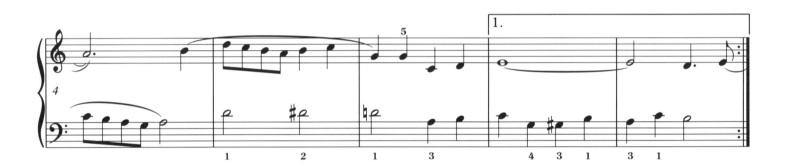

'As Time Goes By' is probably best known because it was used in a film called *Casablanca*. It is sung in the film by a character called Sam, a nightclub pianist. The actor who played Sam could not play the piano, and it was really played by someone else who was hidden behind a curtain.

This is a lovely dreamy tune, but watch out for the accidentals (sharps, flats and naturals). Always keep looking ahead to see what's coming. It would be worth practising this hands separately for a while, until you really know each part well.

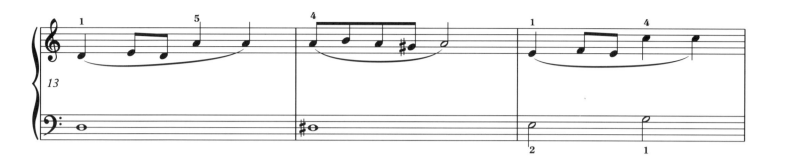

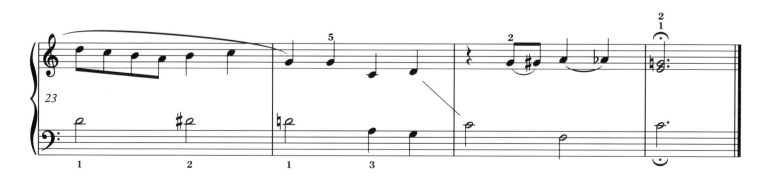

Little brown jug

Traditional

This is a traditional song that is all about the joys and perils of drinking too much. It was made popular by the Weatherwax Brothers Quartet in 1911, and was revived by Glenn Miller and his orchestra in 1939 in an arrangement by Bill Finegan; a recording of which became Miller's first million seller.

You may find this piece quite challenging. Articulation is the important thing to remember; try to observe as many of the marks as possible. Have fun with the long crescendo in the first four bars, but notice that although the right hand is *staccato* (short, detached), the left hand should be *legato* (long, smooth).

Printed and bound in Great Britain